THiS BOOK BELONGS TO:

_____

_____

_____

A. A. Milne
—THE—
POOH
BIRTHDAY BOOK

Illustrated by E.H.Shepard

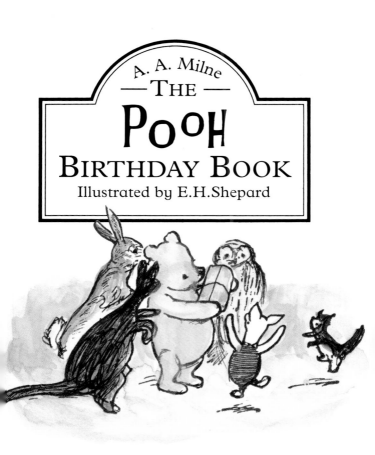

DEAN

First published in Great Britain 1985
by Methuen Children's Books
This edition first published 1997
Reprinted 1999
by Dean
an imprint of Egmont Children's Books Limited
239 Kensington High Street, London W8 6SA

1 3 5 7 9 10 8 6 4 2

Produced by Wing King Tong
Printed and bound in China
ISBN 0 603 55992 1

JANUARY

1 _____

2 _____

3 _____

4 _____

5 _____

6 _____

7 _____

JANUARY

So Owl wrote...
and this is what he wrote:

HiPy PAPy BThUTHDTH
THUTHDA
BThUTHDy.

JANUARY

8 _____

9 _____

10 _____

11 _____

12 _____

13 _____

14 _____

JANUARY

JANUARY

The more it
SNOWS-tiddely-pom...

JANUARY

15 _____

16 _____

17 _____

18 _____

19 _____

20 _____

21 _____

JANUARY

22 _____

23 _____

24 _____

25 _____

26 _____

27 _____

28 _____

JANUARY

So they went on,
feeling just a little anxious now,
in case the three animals in front
of them were of Hostile Intent.
And Piglet wished very much
that his Grandfather T. W. were there,
instead of elsewhere, and Pooh thought
how nice it would be if they met
Christopher Robin suddenly
but quite accidentally, and only
because he liked Christopher Robin so much.

JANUARY

29 _____

30 _____

31 _____

"I see now," said
Winnie-the-Pooh.
"I have been Foolish
and Deluded," said he,
"and I am a Bear
of No Brain at All."

FEBRUARY

"Eeyore," said Owl,
"Christopher Robin
is giving a party."

"Very interesting," said Eeyore.
"I suppose they will be
sending me down the odd bits
which got trodden on.
Kind and Thoughtful.
Not at all, don't mention it."

FEBRUARY

1 _____

2 _____

3 _____

4 _____

5 _____

6 _____

7 _____

FEBRUARY

8 _____

9 _____

10 _____

11 _____

12 _____

13 _____

14 _____

FEBRUARY

He got out of bed
and opened his front door.
"Hallo!" said Pooh,
in case there was anything outside.

"Hallo!" said Whatever-it-was.

"Oh!" said Pooh. "Hallo!"

FEBRUARY

15 _____

16 _____

17 _____

18 _____

19 _____

20 _____

21 _____

FEBRUARY

"Tracks," said Piglet. "Paw-marks."
He gave a little squeak of excitement.
"Oh, Pooh! Do you think it's
a-a-a Woozle?"

"It may be," said Pooh.
"Sometimes it is,
and sometimes it isn't.
You can never tell
with paw-marks."

FEBRUARY

"Is this it?" said Eeyore, a little surprised.
Piglet nodded.
"My present?"
Piglet nodded again.
"The balloon?"
"Yes, Eeyore," said Piglet, sniffing a little.
"Here it is.

FEBRUARY

22 _____

23 _____

24 _____

25 _____

With – many happy returns of the day."
And he gave Eeyore the small piece of damp rag.

FEBRUARY

26 _____

27 _____

28 _____

29 _____

FEBRUARY

Pooh tried to think,
and all he could think of
was something which didn't help at all.
So he hummed it very quietly to himself.
If Rabbit
Was bigger
And fatter
And stronger,
Or bigger
Than Tigger,
If Tigger was smaller,
Then Tigger's bad habit
Of bouncing at Rabbit
Would matter
No longer,
If Rabbit
Was taller.

MARCH

1 _____

2 _____

3 _____

4 _____

5 _____

6 _____

7 _____

MARCH

"Good-bye," said Eeyore.
"Mind you don't get blown away, little Piglet.

You'd be missed.
People would say
'Where's little Piglet
been blown to?' -
really wanting to know.

Well, good-bye.
And thank you
for happening to pass me."

MARCH

Kanga was down below
tying the things on,
and calling out to Owl,
"You won't want this
dirty old dish-cloth any more,
will you, and what about this carpet,
it's all in holes,"
and Owl was calling back
indignantly, "Of course I do!
It's just a question of
arranging the furniture properly,
and it isn't a dish-cloth,
it's my shawl."

MARCH

8 _____

9 _____

10 _____

11 _____

12 _____

13 _____

14 _____

MARCH

"Supposing a tree fell down, Pooh,
when we were underneath it?"

"Supposing it didn't,"
said Pooh after careful thought.

Piglet was comforted by this.

MARCH

15 _____

16 _____

17 _____

18 _____

MARCH

19 _____

20 _____

21 _____

22 _____

23 _____

24 _____

25 _____

MARCH

"Pooh," said Owl severely, "did *you* do that?"

"No," said Pooh humbly. "I don't *think* so."

"Then who did?"

"I think it was the wind," said Piglet. "I think your house has blown down."

As soon as he got home, he went to the larder;
and he stood on a chair, and took down
a very large jar of honey from the top shelf.

It had HUNNY written on it, but,
just to make sure, he took off the paper cover
and looked at it, and it *looked* just like honey.

MARCH

26 _____

27 _____

28 _____

29 _____

30 _____

31 _____

APRIL

1 _____

2 _____

3 _____

4 _____

5 _____

6 _____

7 _____

APRIL

Kanga and Roo
were spending a quiet afternoon
in a sandy part of the Forest.
Baby Roo was practising
very small jumps in the sand,
and falling down mouse holes
and climbing out of them,
and Kanga was fidgeting about
and saying, "Just one more jump,
dear, and then we must go home."
And at that moment
who should come stumping
up the hill but Pooh.

APRIL

When he awoke in the morning,
the first thing he saw was Tigger,
sitting in front of the glass
and looking at himself.

"Hallo!" said Pooh.

"Hallo!" said Tigger.

"I've found somebody just like me.
I thought I was the only one of them."

APRIL

8

9

10

11

12

13

APRiL

Christopher Robin gave a deep sigh,
picked his Bear up by the leg,
and walked off to the door,
trailing Pooh behind him.
At the door he turned and said,
"Coming to see me have my bath?"
"I might," I said.

APRIL

14 _____

15 _____

16 _____

17 _____

18 _____

19 _____

20 _____

APRIL

21 _____

22 _____

23 _____

24 _____

25 _____

26 _____

27 _____

APRIL

APRIL

28 _____

29 _____

30 _____

Owl lived at The Chestnuts,
an old-world residence of great charm,
which was grander than anybody else's,
or seemed so to Bear, because it had
both a knocker *and* a bell-pull.
Underneath the knocker there was a notice
which said:

PLES RING iF AN RNSER iS REQIRD.

Underneath the bell-pull
there was a notice which said:

PLEZ CNOKE iF AN RNSR iS NOT REQID.

APRIL

MAY

1 _____

2 _____

3 _____

4 _____

5 _____

6 _____

7 _____

MAY

Tigger took a large mouthful of honey
...and he looked up at the ceiling
with his head on one side,
and made exploring noises with his tongue,
and considering noises,
and what-have-we-got-*here* noises
...and then he said in a very decided voice:
"Tiggers don't like honey."

MAY

MAY

8 _____

9 _____

10 _____

11 _____

12 _____

MAY

13 _____

14 _____

15 _____

16 _____

17 _____

18 _____

19 _____

MAY

MAY

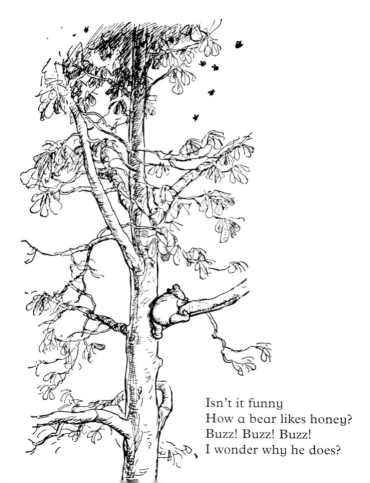

Isn't it funny
How a bear likes honey?
Buzz! Buzz! Buzz!
I wonder why he does?

MAY

20

21

22

23

24

MAY

"*Ow!*" said Pooh.

"Did I miss?" you asked.

"You didn't exactly *miss*," said Pooh,
"but you missed the *balloon*."

MAY

25 _____

26 _____

27 _____

28 _____

29 _____

30 _____

31 _____

JUNE

1 _____

2 _____

3 _____

4 _____

5 _____

6 _____

7 _____

JUNE

"Can't you *see*?" shouted Piglet.
"Haven't you got *eyes*?
Look at me!"

"I *am* looking, Roo, dear,"
said Kanga rather severely.
And you know what I told you
yesterday about making faces.
If you go on making faces
like Piglet's, you will grow up
to *look* like Piglet - and *then*
think how sorry you will be.
Now then, into the bath,
and don't let me have to
speak to you about it again."

"I *think* Heffalumps come
if you whistle."
"Some do and some don't.
You never can tell
with Heffalumps."

JUNE

8

9

10

11

12

13

14

JUNE

I could spend a happy morning
  Seeing Roo,
I could spend a happy morning
  Being Pooh.
For it doesn't seem to matter,
If I don't get any fatter
(And I *don't* get any fatter),
  What I do.

JUNE

15 _____

16 _____

17 _____

18 _____

19 _____

20 _____

21 _____

JUNE

22 _____

23 _____

24 _____

25 _____

26 _____

"Tigger is all right, *really*," said Piglet lazily.
"Of course he is," said Christopher Robin.
"Everybody is *really*," said Pooh. "That's what *I* think,"
said Pooh. "But I don't suppose I'm right," he said.
"Of course you are," said Christopher Robin.

JUNE

27

_____

28

_____

29

_____

30

_____

JUNE

"Look, Pooh!" said Piglet suddenly.
"There's something in one of the Pine Trees."

"So there is!" said Pooh,
looking up wonderingly.
"There's an Animal."

Piglet took Pooh's arm,
in case Pooh was frightened.

"Is it One of the Fiercer Animals?"
he said, looking the other way.

Pooh nodded.
"It's a Jagular," he said.

JULY

1 _____

2 _____

3 _____

4 _____

5 _____

6 _____

7 _____

JULY

"Hallo, are you stuck?" he asked.
"N-no," said Pooh carelessly.
"Just resting
and thinking
and humming to myself."

JULY

"After all," said Rabbit to himself,
"Christopher Robin depends on Me.
He's fond of Pooh
and Piglet
and Eeyore,
and so am I,
but they haven't any Brain."

JULY

8

9

10

11

12

13

14

JULY

JULY

"Eeyore," he said solemnly,
"I, Winnie-the-Pooh,
will find your tail for you."
"Thank you, Pooh," answered Eeyore.
"You're a real friend," said he.
"Not Like Some," he said.

15
_____

16
_____

17
_____

18
_____

19
_____

JULY

20 _____

21 _____

22 _____

23 _____

24 _____

25 _____

26 _____

JULY

Who found the Tail?
   "I," said Pooh,
"At a quarter to two
   (Only it was quarter to eleven really),
I found the Tail!"

JULY

JULY

Eeyore frisked about the forest,
waving his tail so happily
that Winnie-the-Pooh came over all funny,
and had to hurry home
for a little snack of something to sustain him.

27
_____

28
_____

29
_____

30
_____

31
_____

AUGUST

1 _____

2 _____

3 _____

4 _____

5 _____

They all went off to discover the Pole,
  Owl and Piglet and Rabbit and all;
It's a Thing you Discover, as I've been tole
  By Owl and Piglet and Rabbit and all.
Eeyore, Christopher Robin and Pooh
And Rabbit's relations all went too –
And where the Pole was none of them knew
  Sing Hey! for Owl and Rabbit and all!

AUGUST

AUGUST

6 _____

7 _____

8 _____

9 _____

10 _____

11 _____

12 _____

AUGUST

"Hello, Rabbit," he said,
"is that you?"

"Let's pretend it isn't,"
said Rabbit, "and see what happens."

AUGUST

"*Hush!*" said Eeyore in a terrible voice
to all Rabbit's friends-and-relations,
and "Hush!" they said hastily to
each other all down the line,
until it got to the last one of all.
And the last and smallest
friend-and-relation was so upset
to find that the whole Expotition
was saying "Hush!" to *him*,
that he buried himself head downwards
in a crack in the ground,

and stayed there for two days
until the danger was over,
and then went home in a great hurry,
and lived quietly with his Aunt ever-afterwards.
His name was Alexander Beetle.

AUGUST

13 _____

14 _____

15 _____

16 _____

17 _____

18 _____

19 _____

AUGUST

20 _____

21 _____

22 _____

23 _____

24 _____

25 _____

26 _____

AUGUST

AUGUST

August

27 _____

28 _____

29 _____

30 _____

31 _____

"I'm not asking anybody," said Eeyore.
"I'm just telling everybody.
We can look for the North Pole,
or we can play 'Here we go
gathering Nuts and May'
with the end part of an ants' nest.
It's all the same to me."

SEPTEMBER

1 _____

2 _____

3 _____

4 _____

Shall I look, too?" said Pooh,
who was beginning to feel
a little eleven o' clockish.
And he found a small tin
of condensed milk, and something
seemed to tell him that Tiggers
didn't like this, so he took it
into a corner by itself,
and went with it to see
that nobody interrupted it.

SEPTEMBER

Tra-la-la, tra-la-la,
Tra-la-la, tra-la-la,
Rum-tum-tiddle-um-tum.
Tiddle-iddle, tiddle-iddle,
Tiddle-iddle, tiddle-iddle,
Rum-tum-tum-tiddle-um.

SEPTEMBER

5 _____

6 _____

7 _____

8 _____

9 _____

10 _____

11 _____

SEPTEMBER

12 _____

13 _____

14 _____

15 _____

16 _____

He looked up at his clock,
which had stopped at five minutes
to eleven some weeks ago.
"Nearly eleven o'clock," said Pooh happily.
"You're just in time
for a little smackerel of something."

SEPTEMBER

SEPTEMBER.

SEPTEMBER

17

18

19

20

21

22

23

SEPTEMBER

24 _____

25 _____

26 _____

27 _____

28 _____

29 _____

30 _____

SEPTEMBER

OCTOBER.

OCTOBER

1 _____

2 _____

3 _____

4 _____

5 _____

6 _____

7 _____

OCTOBER

8
_____

9
_____

"You only blinched inside," said Pooh,
"and that's the bravest way for a
Very Small Animal not to blinch
that there is."

Piglet sighed with happiness,
and began to think about himself.
He was BRAVE...

10
_____

11
_____

OCTOBER

12 _____

13 _____

14 _____

15 _____

16 _____

17 _____

18 _____

OCTOBER

"I am calling it this,"
said Owl importantly,
and he showed them
what he had been making.
It was a square piece of board
with the name of the house painted on it:

THE WOLERY

OCTOBER

19 _____

20 _____

IT'S ME PIGLIT, HELP HELP!

21 _____

22 _____

23 _____

24 _____

OCTOBER.

OCTOBER

OCTOBER

25

_____

26

_____

27

_____

28

_____

29

_____

30

_____

31

_____

NOVEMBER.

NOVEMBER

1

2

"We might go in your umbrella," said Pooh.
"?"

"We might go in your umbrella," said Pooh.
"??"

"We might go in your umbrella," said Pooh.
"!!!!!!"

For suddenly Christopher Robin saw
that they might. He opened his umbrella
and put it point downwards in the water.
It floated but wobbled.

3

4

NOVEMBER,

5 _____

6 _____

7 _____

8 _____

9 _____

10 _____

11 _____

NOVEMBER

NOVEMBER.

NOVEMBER

12 _____

13 _____

14 _____

15 _____

16 _____

17 _____

18 _____

NOVEMBER

19 _____

20 _____

21 _____

"Oh, there you are,"
said Christopher Robin carelessly,
trying to pretend that he hadn't been Anxious.

22 _____

23 _____

24 _____

NOVEMBER

NOVEMBER.

NOVEMBER

25 _____

26 _____

27 _____

28 _____

29 _____

30 _____

DECEMBER

1 _____

2 _____

3 _____

4 _____

5 _____

6 _____

7 _____

DECEMBER.

"Yes," said Pooh.
"We had breakfast together
yesterday.
By the Pine Trees.
I'd made up
a little basket,

just a little,
fair-sized basket,

an ordinary
biggish sort of basket,
full of – "

DECEMBER.

eOR

DECEMBER

8 _____

9 _____

10 _____

Eeyore was saying to himself,
"This writing business.
Pencils and what-not.
Over-rated, if you ask me.
Silly stuff.
Nothing in it."

11 _____

12 _____

DECEMBER

13 _____

14 _____

"Ha!" said Rabbit,
feeling quite happy again.
"Another notice!"
This is what it said:

GON OUT
BACKSON
BISY
BACKSON   C.R..

15 _____

16 _____

17 _____

DECEMBER

DECEMBER

18 _____

19 _____

20 _____

21 _____

22 _____

23 _____

24 _____

DECEMBER.

Kanga

WOL

Pooh

Piglet

Rabbit.

DECEMBER.

25 _____

26 _____

27 _____

28 _____

29 _____

30 _____

31 _____